Contents — Open string viola part

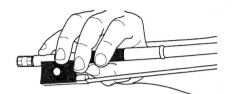

Sing, clap or march with the tune and **feel the beat** before playing on your viola.

Play **A** string

See saw, Margery Daw,
Johnny shall have a new master.
He shall have but a penny a day,
Because he can't work any faster.

Play **A** or **D** string

Weel may the keel row,
The keel row, the keel row,
Weel may the keel row,
The ship my laddie's in.

Play **A** string

London Bridge is falling down,
Falling down, falling down,
London Bridge is falling down,
My fair lady.

Play **D** or **D A**

Grandma Grunts said a curious thing,
'Boys can whistle but girls must sing.'
This is what I heard her say,
'Twas no longer than yesterday.

Play **D**

Are you sleeping, are you sleeping,
Brother John, Brother John?
Morning bells are ringing, morning bells are ringing,
Ding, ding, dong, ding, ding, dong.

Play **D**

Mammy's little baby loves shortnin' shortnin',
Mammy's little baby loves shortnin' bread,
Mammy's little baby loves shortnin' shortnin',
Mammy's little baby loves shortnin' bread,

Play **G**

Cobbler, cobbler, mend my shoe,
Have it done by half-past two.

Play **G**

Everybody playing, this way, that way,
Everybody playing, this way too.

3

Play **G** or **C**

Rain, rain, go away,
Come again another day.

Play **C**

Ring-a-ring o' roses,
A pocket full of posies,
A-tishoo, a-tishoo!
We all fall down.

Play **C** or **D**

Row, row, row your boat,
Gently down the stream,
Merrily, merrily, merrily, merrily,
Life is but a dream.

Jinglers

G G C C

G D A D

G G C C

G D G G

Hey, diddle diddle

G	G	D	D
Hey, diddle	diddle, the	cat and the	fiddle, the

G	G	D	D
cow jumped	over the	moon_____	, The

C	C	G	G
little dog	laughed to	see such	fun, and the

D	D	G
dish ran a	- way with the	spoon.

Yankee Doodle

G	D	G	D
Yankee	Doodle	went to	town up-

G	D	G	D
on a	little	po -	ny, He

G	G	C	C
stuck a	feather	in his	cap and

D	D	G	G
called it	maca -	ro -	ni.

Merry-go-round

The mulberry bush

Here we go round the   mulberry bush, the   mulberry bush, the   mulberry bush,

Here we go round the   mulberry bush, so   early   in the   morn - ing.

Pop! goes the weasel

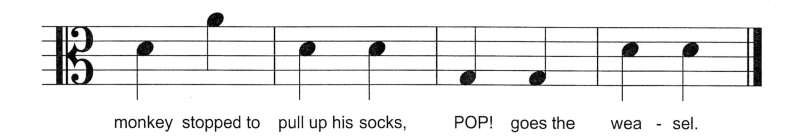

All a - round the cobbler's bench the monkey chased the wea - sel, The

monkey stopped to pull up his socks, POP! goes the wea - sel.

The Muffin Man

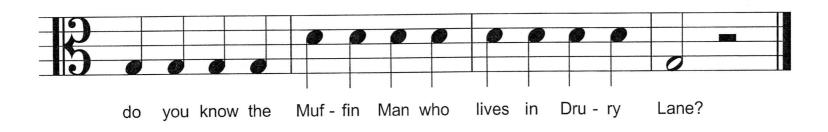

Lightly row

Light - ly row,   light - ly row,   O'er the glas - sy   waves we go.

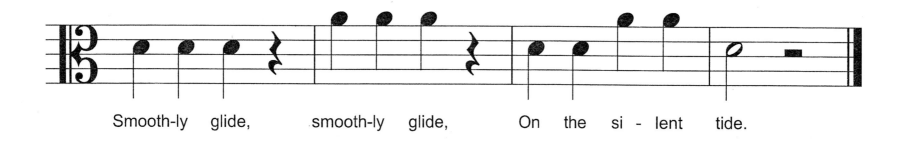

Smooth-ly glide,   smooth-ly glide,   On the si - lent tide.

Minka

Merrily we roll along

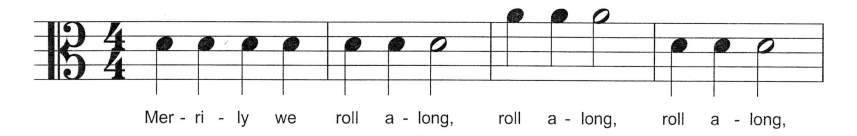

Mer - ri - ly   we   roll   a - long,   roll   a - long,   roll   a - long,

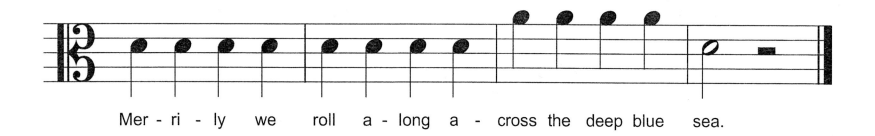

Mer - ri - ly   we   roll   a - long a - cross the deep blue   sea.

Turkey in the straw

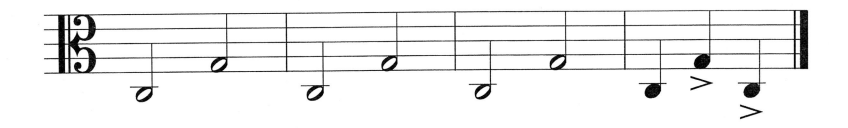

Skip to my Lou

Choose your part - ners, skip to my Lou, Choose your part - ners, skip to my Lou,

Choose your part - ners, skip to my Lou, Skip to my Lou my dar - ling.

Country dance

Where is Sally?

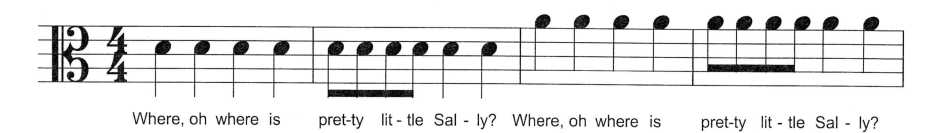

Where, oh where is   pret-ty lit - tle Sal - ly? Where, oh where is   pret-ty lit - tle Sal - ly?

Where, oh where is   pret-ty lit - tle Sal - ly? Way down yon-der in the   paw-paw patch.

The Irish washerwoman

Silent night

Tum balalaika

Bobby Shafto

Bobby Shafto's gone to sea,   Silver buckles   on his knee;

He'll come back and marry   me,   Bonny Bobby   Shaf - to.

Bobby Shafto's   bright and fair, Combing down his   yellow hair;

He's my ain for   evermair,   Bonny   Bobby   Shaf - to.

The tailor and the mouse

There was a tailor had a mouse, Hi diddle unkum fee - dle. They

lived to - gether in one house, Hi diddle unkum fee - dle.

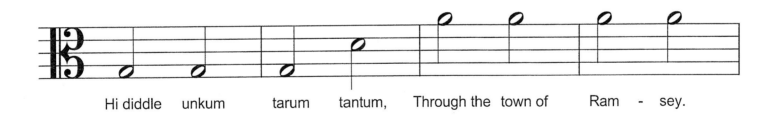

Hi diddle unkum tarum tantum, Through the town of Ram - sey.

Hi diddle unkum over the lea, Hi diddle unkum feedle.

Reap the flax

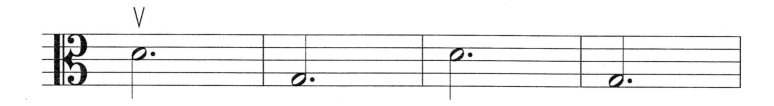